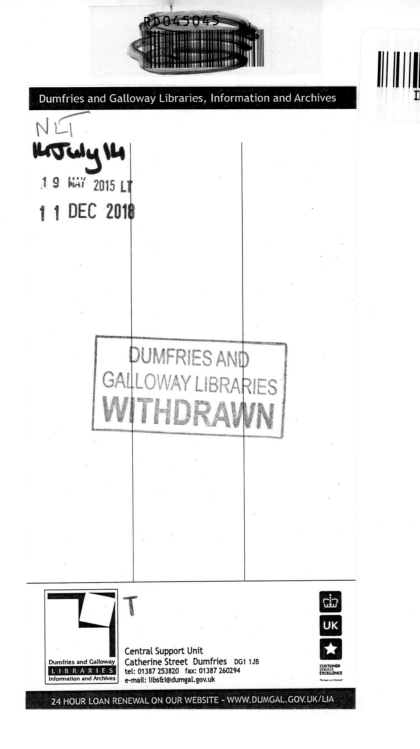

SKINT!

Script by Gowan Calder

Illustrations by Metaphrog

Scottish Book Trust

First published in 2011 in Great Britain by
Scottish Book Trust, Sandeman House, Trunk's Close,
55 High Street, Edinburgh EH1 1SR, Scotland, UK

In partnership with the Scottish Government

ISBN 978-1-901077-254 Free

Typeset, cover art and design by Metaphrog
Skint! title font: Busted by Canada Type

Printed and bound in the EU, by arrangement with Waverley Books Ltd

Contents

Foreword

Scottish Book Trust, in partnership with the Scottish Government, has developed *Skint!* an interactive book for use within facilitated groups of 16-to-26-year-olds.

- *Skint!* consists of two illustrated storylines that explore issues around money management and responsibility.

- The stories have been created to engage reluctant readers and focus on realistic, financial circumstances.

- The endings are intentionally ambiguous giving readers a choice of conclusions (therefore enabling learner-centred education).

- *Skint!* can be read as a group, one to one or used in a variety of role play scenarios.

- Throughout *Skint!* there are opportunities to pause and discuss the situations the characters find themselves in.

- Support workers can lead these discussions and draw upon real-life examples, as well as further background information, from the support notes located at the following web address:

  www.scottishbooktrust.com/skint

- Numerical activities can be completed by the reader, at appropriate points, so enabling applications, such as adding, subtracting, ratios and percentages, to be transferred into a variety of real-life contexts.

- Readers can increase their literacy skills further through creative responses to the stories, by developing alternative storylines and endings.

- Finally, words and meanings can be explored by using the glossary and financial definitions located on pages 102-7.

Access Considerations

A signed and audio version of *Skint!* can be found on the Scottish Book Trust's website:

  www.scottishbooktrust.com/skint

Examples of Additional Materials to Develop the Work

- In facilitator-led groups, preparatory discussions about the characters and storylines can take place by following the illustrations in advance of reading the text.

- Individuals can be encouraged to practise reading independently and/or increase their confidence in reading out loud in a group, by employing the text in a role play scenario. However it is important to be aware that young people are not put on the spot with reading if you are unsure of their reading confidence.

- The storylines can be applied to support and stimulate discussions about money management and used as an incentive to develop problem solving abilities. Images contained in circles have been placed throughout *Skint!* as suggested discussion/activity points and these images link to the equivalent images in the support notes located on the website www.scottishbooktrust.com/skint

- Support workers should use their discretion to select the most suitable activity ideas and discussion topics, according to an individual's and/or groups' needs.
  - Numerical activity ideas could include, for example, using budgeting sheets, percentages, decimal fractions, everyday calculations that directly link to the storylines such as 'would Carly purchase the sofa if she had worked out the true costs including APR?'
  - Creative writing follow up ideas could consist of 'create your own ending', 'introduce a new character' and 'create a new storyline' at certain points.

- Support workers can introduce activities around filling in forms (such as tax forms or, for prison settings, personal allowance forms) as linked to appropriate parts of the storylines in *Skint!* They should select forms from relevant websites as befits their group's needs. Suggested web links are provided in the support notes on the website www.scottishbooktrust.com/skint and on page 112.

- Furthermore, support workers can select from a series of complementary resources, for example 'comic life'.

- Support workers are also encouraged to develop their own materials, as appropriate, and to use 'reflecting questions' with their groups to consolidate what has been learnt/covered.

- Finally, the support notes provide a check sheet indicating which of the achievements, as detailed in the core literacy and numeracy curriculum can be covered by using *Skint!*

Character Biographies

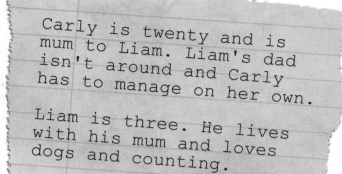

Carly is twenty and is mum to Liam. Liam's dad isn't around and Carly has to manage on her own.

Liam is three. He lives with his mum and loves dogs and counting.

Dani is eighteen. She has just started at university where she is studying Engineering.

May is a single mother. She is Dani's mum and Jamie's aunt.

Kim owns a cafe. She is married but has no children. She sees enough of them at work!

Angie is a full-time mum. She is Damien's mum and has three other boys.

The Salesman from House Heaven.

Mushtak runs the local newsagent's. He comes from Iran where he was a journalist before seeking political asylum in Britain.

Jamie is twenty-two. He has just come home after spending a few months in a Young Offenders unit.

Damien is seventeen. He is attending Catering College and wants to be a chef.

Davey and Jamie grew up together. He usually means trouble...

Tam likes betting on the horses and a good pint. Rumour has it he once won the lottery.

Brian recently lost his business and now looks after the house and his two kids while his wife is working.

Pavel runs the local pub, The Stag's Head. His family is from Poland.

'Scruffy' is a stray who keeps an eye on the folks in the street with his wee dog pal.

Carly's Story - In For a Penny, In For a Pound

Monday - £8.23

Kim's Kafé: Kim stands at her counter while Angie has a fag at the doorway, watching the street.

Angie: There's Carly and her wee boy outside that new House Heaven shop.

Kim: Well, I hope she's not going to go in.

Angie: They've got lovely things in there, but.

Kim: Aye, and lovely prices too.

Angie: But it's all weekly payments. You don't have to pay for it all at once.

Kim: My mother always said - 'Never go on the Never-Never'.

Angie: Eh?

Kim: My mother did not believe in credit.

Angie: Aye? Good for her, but my boys would have nothing if I didn't have credit.

Kim: It'll catch up with you, Angie, mark my words...

Angie: Yes, 'Mother'.

Kim: And get away from my door - you're smoking up the place.

Angie: You know what you are, Kim? You are what my Damien calls a 'Funpire'.

Kim: A what?

Angie: A Funpire - someone who sucks all the fun out of life... Like a vampire, get it?

Kim: Oh, very amusing. But my café, my rules!

Carly stands outside House Heaven, her son, Liam, is in his pushchair. A dog pees nearby.

Carly: There it is, Liam - the dream sofa. The Princess Three-Seater. Awesome, no?

Liam: Doggie?

Carly: No Liam, sofa - can you say sofa?

Liam: Sweetie!

Carly: Maybe later, eh? Look, Liam, look at the sofa! Pure. Dead. Gorgeous.

Liam: Gujus.

Carly: Know the snotty cow who lives next door? She's only got the Duchess Two-Seater...

Liam: Moo-cow?

Carly: She'd be spewin' if I got the three-seater, eh?

Liam: Moo!

Carly: Aye, snotty cow goes 'Moo'! Better go talk to that man at the Jobcentre now, eh?

Liam: Bye-bye sofa.

Carly: Aye, clever boy! Bye-bye sofa.

Liam: I'm free.

Carly: That's right, you're three. You're good at counting, you are.

Liam: One, two, free...

Carly: Maybe you could get a job at the bookies, eh?

They walk down the street, followed by the dog.

Kim's Kafé: Angie stands and chats with Kim.

Kim: Do you fancy another coffee, there, Angie?

Angie: On the house is it, Kim? Buy one get one free?

Kim: Beg your pardon? Tell me, Angie, can you see that sign up there?

Angie: 'You don't have to be mad to work here, but it helps'?

Kim: Not that one – the one next to it.

Angie: 'Please don't ask for credit as a smack in the mouth often offends'?

Kim: That's the one. I'm running a business here, Angie – not a charity.

Angie: Here, I know what you mean. My Damien thinks I'm a free money machine.

Kim: You just have to say 'no' to them, Angie.

Angie: It's hard when their pals get new stuff, but. They get new trainers and Damien wants them...

Kim: And I bet it's not the cheap ones he's after.

Angie: Too right – they cost eighty pound.

Kim: You'll have to save up for them then, eh?

Angie: I'll have that coffee now please, Kim. And a a wee caramel slice as well.

Kim: And what about those trainers for your lad?

Angie: Told you – credit card...

Kim: Not in here, you won't – that'll be £1.60, in cash, please.

13

May comes into Kim's Kafé.

May: Morning all. Hey Angie, I just saw your Damien. That boy likes his bling, eh?

Angie: Oh, don't you start, May. You remember what it's like to be young.

May: Aye – I remember the shame of wearing a mingin duffel coat my ma bought with Co-op stamps.

Kim: Well, my ma made us clothes out of the curtains. She'd never pay £80 for a pair of shoes.

May: That's nothing. I bought Dani an iPhone the other day. Cost the same as this month's rent!

Kim: You two spoil your kids rotten.

Angie: See, I'd love one of them. They're better than kids, they are. Want a hot bath?

May: There's an App for that!

Angie: Want a Bacardi Breezer and a *Hello* magazine?

May: There's an App for that! Want a free takeaway coffee from Kim's Kafé?

Kim: You can kiss my Apps.

May: Worth a try. I'd better go and sign on.

Technology costs?

The Jobcentre: May chats to Carly. We can also see Brian and Jamie waiting their turn.

May: Hiya Carly, how you doing?

Carly: Oh, you know, getting by.

May: Aye, it must be hard with the wee one. They cost money, eh?

Carly: Aye, good thing Liam likes beans on toast. I've got £8.23 to last us until my giro comes in.

May: Does Liam's dad not help out?

Carly: No chance. I wouldn't mind a job, like, but what am I supposed to do with Liam?

May: Aye, there's not many jobs that fit in with looking after a wee one.

Carly: The guy asked me today what kind of work I'd be interested in. I said I want to be a WAG.

May: Did he laugh?

Carly: No, he told me there's jobs going in ASDA.

May: Well they do have some nice handbags...

Carly: Yeah, I'm sure I saw Cheryl Cole buying one in there the other day.

May: Aye right! Never mind doll, your luck will change.

Carly: I'm not the lucky kind, May.

May: Trust me, I've got a sixth sense. I'm never wrong about these things.

Carly and Liam are in the newsagent's. Liam is crying.

Mushtak: Here he is. How's wee Liam today?

Liam: Sweetie!

Carly: No darlin', not just now.

Liam: Sweetie, sweetie, sweetie, sweetie!

Carly: Sorry Mushtak – just this juice thanks.

Mushtak: It's hard when they're wee, eh? That's 45p
please, Carly.

Carly checks the money in her purse.

Carly: You know, I'll take a scratch card as well.

Mushtak: Feeling lucky, eh?

Carly: Yeah, that May said my luck will change.

Liam: Nana.

Carly: Oh no, where did you get that from?

Mushtak: That's okay, he can have it.

Carly: Give mammy the banana, Liam... Now!

Mushtak: It's fine, Carly. He can pay me back when he
starts his paper round, eh?

Carly: He doesn't need it. He gets fed. I feed him!

Mushtak: Of course you do. You're a good mum.

Carly: He gets clothes on his back and three meals a
a day. He doesn't need to steal bananas!

Mushtak: He's eaten half of it, Carly. Let him have it.

Carly: How much is it, then?

Mushtak: 10p.

Carly: No it's not.

Mushtak: Okay, 5p. Deal or no deal?

Carly: We don't need charity.

Mushtak: It's today's special offer. Deal or no deal?

Carly: ... Deal... Thanks, Mushtak.

Mushtak: No bother, have a good night.

Carly: We're off to the park, eh, Liam? For a wee picnic.

They leave the shop. As they leave, Jamie and Brian come in.

Jamie: Hiya Liam, my wee pal. How you doing?

Liam: Sweetie?

Carly: How many times, Liam? No!

Liam starts screaming again.

Sorry, Jamie... See you later.

Carly and Liam are outside the charity shop. Carly is putting Liam's shoe on.

Carly: You've got to keep your shoes on, pal. Mammy can't afford new ones right now.

Liam points at the shop window.

Liam: Sooos?

Carly: That's right, but mammy doesn't like manky old things. You don't know where they've been.

May comes out of the shop.

May: Hey, are you pair following me?

Carly: No.

May: Only joking, doll. I've just got the best wee T-shirt for Dani and it was only 50p.

May shows Carly the T-shirt.

Carly: Nice.

May: Naw, it's weird – but Dani will like it. She likes to be original, eh?

Carly: I know. I got a row for calling her a Goth once.

May: Oh, big mistake! She's no an Emo, either, like.

Carly: I know, she told me that too...

May: Did you see those wee Doc Martens in the window? They'd be perfect for the wee one...

Carly: He doesn't need shoes.

May: What, a growing boy like Liam? He must need stuff all the time...

Carly: He's fine. See you later, May.

Keeping up
appearances?

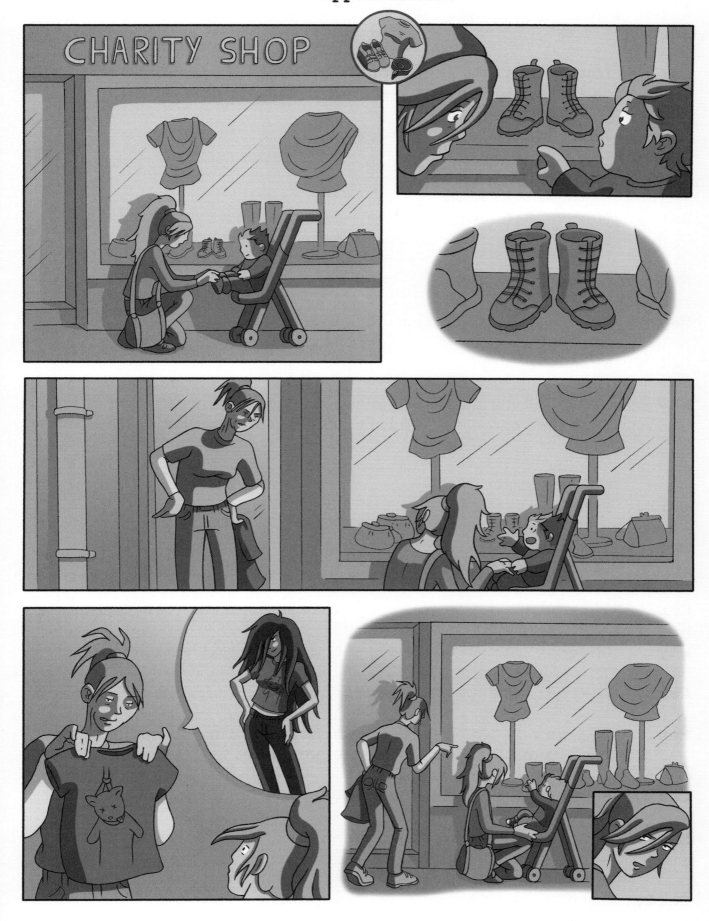

May: Do you not fancy a wee coffee at the café? I'm off there for a wee gossip...

Carly: No money.

May: Kim does a special – £1.60 for coffee and a bun. You need a wee treat.

Carly: Look – I'm fine, Liam's fine... We're all fine, okay?

May: Okay... I'll see you later.

Carly takes off with Liam. We see Liam's shoe on the ground. The scruffy dog comes and sniffs it then picks it up in his mouth. Carly stops outside House Heaven and looks in the window again.

Liam: Mama?

Carly: What? That old witch is always turning up and nagging me... Look, here's my sofa.

Liam: Sooos.

Carly: It says '156 easy payments of £8.79 a week'. Sounds easy enough...

Liam: Sooos, mama?

Carly: We've got £6.73. How much more do we need for a down payment, clever boy?

Liam: Free?

Kim's Kafé: May enters, followed by the dog with the shoe in his mouth.

Kim: Hey you, out of here!

May: Charming.

Kim: Not you, May — that manky dog. He stole a muffin from poor old Mrs Murray yesterday.

Angie: And this is a business, May — no a charity.

May: Talking of charity — I got a lovely T-shirt for Dani over in the shop there.

Angie: Does she not mind wearing second-hand?

May: Naw — she calls it 'vintage'. Vintage is trendy, don't ya know?

Dani enters.

May: Talk of the devil, here she is now.

Kim: I said, OUT!

Dani: What? What have I done now?

Kim: Not you, pet, the dog. What can I get you, Dani?

Dani: I'll have a grandee, extra-hot, non-fat, soy milk latte with sprinkles, please.

Kim: Come again?

May: She'll have a milky coffee, Kim.

Kim: Why could she not just say so?

May: Are you going to have lunch with us, Dani?

Dani: I'd rather chew my own arm off, thanks.

Angie: Oi, you should be nice to your mum since she bought you that iPhone.

Dani: She only paid for half of it so I only have to be nice half the time.

May: She saved the rest with the credit union at her college.

Kim: See, that's what we used to do in the old days, Angie. We used to save up for what we wanted.

Angie: Aye, but it's hard to save when you've no money, Kim.

Kim: My mother used to say, 'look after the pennies and the pounds will look after themselves'.

Angie: Aye, your ma was a great laugh.

May: You know what? We should start a menodge.

Dani: A what?

May: It's like a savings club. Everyone puts money in every week.

Angie: And every month someone different wins it, see?

Dani: How does that work? What if you never win?

Angie: Ocht, we nearly always spend it on a good night out for everybody in the menodge, anyway.

Dani: 'A Good Night Out Club'? I like it. I might start a Kylie.

May: A what?

Dani: A Kylie. A Kylie Menodge. Can I have that coffee to take away please, Kim?

Dani is looking in the window of House Heaven. The scruffy dog and his wee dog pal sit next to her, doing the same. Damien walks past, holding a six-pack of lager.

Damien: Awright, Dani? Are you planning a spot of shoplifting?

Dani: No, I hate this place.

Damien: My auntie got a telly out of here.

Dani: Then she was ripped off.

Damien: No she wasn't – it's like a tenner a week.

Dani is calculating on her iPhone.

Dani: See that sofa there?

Damien: Aye, I'm not blind.

Dani: It says it's £952.53, right?

Damien: I can read, too.

Dani: Okay – it says 156 repayments of £8.79. How much is that?

Damien: Do I look like a calculator?

Dani: It's £1371.24

Damien: No way, man.

Dani: Way. 29.9% Typical APR.

Damien: Whatever. I'm going up the park. Fancy it, you smartarse?

Dani: Yeah, okay – you pre-historic bottom-feeder.

156 x £8.79 = £1371.24

£952.53

ONLY £952.53

156 EASY
PAYMENTS
OF £8.79
A WEEK!

29.9%
APR

Dani and Damien go off together. The dogs are still looking in the shop window. The big dog is our scruffy doggie hero. The wee one is his terrier pal.

Wee Dog: So, have you got your eye on that 42-inch plasma TV, then?

Big Dog: Naw – I prefer a walk in the park.

Wee Dog: Aye, me too.

Big Dog: I'm off to the pub.

Wee Dog: What for?

Big Dog: To see if anyone's dropped their pork scratchings on the floor. Fancy it?

Wee Dog: Aye, why not? Beats a night in watching River City. I prefer crisps, though.

Big Dog: They drop them too, pal. And we might even get a saucer of Eighty Shilling.

Wee Dog: You had me at 'crisps', mate... What's APR, by the way?

Big Dog: Interest.

Wee Dog: Boring, more like... I fancy a Twiglet, do they have them too?

What's
APR
by the
way?

The park: Dani and Damien are hanging out on the swings.
Carly and Liam sit on a bench. Liam eats his sandwich and
Carly is doing her scratch card.

Dani: So are you liking catering college, then?

Damien: S'alright – can't be bothered with living at
          my mum's, though.

Dani: It's not for long, eh? You'll be a chef soon.

Damien: Aye, but the money's crap when you start.

Dani: Yeah, I'm on £5.93 an hour at the Coffee Shack
          so I can't see me getting a flat any time soon.

Damien: Can you not get more hours?

Dani: Maybe, but I've got so much work to do for uni...

Damien: I thought you were just making things out of
          Lego?

Dani: Yeah, right! I'm studying engineering, doofus.

Damien: I was joking, smartarse.

The scruffy dog has turned up.

Carly: Well, we won nothing on the scratch card, babe.
          There's a surprise, eh?

Liam: Doggie!

Carly: Aye, it's a doggie.

Liam: Hungry doggie?

Carly: No Liam – don't give him your sandwich...! And
          where's your shoe...?

          You're driving me mental, so you are.

Jamie appears. He has Liam's shoe.

Jamie: Hey, Carly, are you looking for this?

Carly: Aye, where did you find it?

Jamie: The dog had it. It's a bit manky, like.

Carly: Great. Now I'm covered in dog slaver... I'm going home.

Jamie: I was going for a poke of chips, if you fancy...?

Carly: Thanks, but I'm not in the mood for chips.

Jamie is left alone with the dog.

Jamie: Smooth, eh dug? Really smooth.

* * *

Dani: I feel like I'll be paying off my student loans and living at my mum's forever.

Damien: I'm gonna go on Deal or No Deal.

Dani: Oh yeah? How much you planning on winning?

Damien: I reckon £250,000 would do me.

Dani: Excellent plan. Good luck with that!

Damien: Have you got a better one, genius?

Dani: I'm going to marry a footballer.

Damien: Yeah – in your dreams!

Dani: Or, I'm going to finish uni and get a job so I don't have to rely on some idiot man like you.

Damien: See, I know you like me really...

Tuesday - £6.73

Carly's flat. She is slumped on a moth-eaten old sofa. Next to her is a plate of burnt toast. Liam plays by her feet. There is a knock on the door.

Carly: There's the door, baby. I wonder who's coming to visit us?

She opens the door.

Man: Carly Macdonald?

Carly: Yeah?

Man: I'm from R.J. Johns Debt Collecting Agency.

Carly: Oh, not you guys again!

Man: It seems you have an outstanding debt with us...

Carly: I told the last guy. I'm sorting it.

Man: You have made no recent payment...

Carly: I didn't understand the Council Tax rebate forms...

Man: And if you do not settle the debt in full we will have to take action.

Carly: But the guy at the Jobcentre helped me and when I get the rebate, I'll pay you.

Man: I'll give you another week, but that's it.

Carly: I'm doing my best...

Man: See you in a week.

Time passes. Carly sits on the sofa, head in hands. She stares out the window. She tidies up. She stares out the window. She sits on the sofa...

Carly: I hate this sofa. I hate this flat. I hate my life.

Liam: Sweetie?

Carly: Aye, why not? We've still got £6.73 – let's go crazy!

**Good debt/
Bad debt?**

In the newsagent's.

Mushtak: Anything else, doll?

Carly: No thanks, just the loaf.

Liam: Sweetie!

Mushtak: Oh, here we go...

Carly: Know what? He's had a rubbish day he deserves a packet of Skittles.

Mushtak: That's £1.59, ta.

Carly: And I'll take a scratch card too, please.

Mushtak: Feeling lucky again, eh?

Carly: Aye, maybe.

VROOOM

Outside the newsagent's: Carly is doing her scratch card.

Carly: Nothing again. A pound wasted. I'm so stupid I could slap myself!

May: Alright there, Carly?

Carly: I'm fine, thank you.

May: Nae luck on the scratchy, eh? I've barred myself from buying them.

Carly: I just get one from time to time.

May: I was addicted to them. I convinced myself they would solve my money problems.

Carly: It's just a pound sometimes.

May: I spent hundreds on them. What a numpty, eh?

Carly: Well, someone has to win...

May: Talking of winning, we're starting our menodge at the café today.

Carly: My mum used to do that. One time she won it we all went to the Girls Aloud concert.

May: Aye, it's a good way to treat ourselves now and again, eh?

Carly: Sorry, May, but I've got about £4 to last us...

May: Then I'll treat us to a coffee, eh? Go on – just come for a natter.

The man from the debt collecting agency passes by and sees Carly. She sees him too.

Carly: Sorry, got to rush! I need to get Liam home.

May: Okay, doll, another time, eh? By the way Liam's kicked off his shoe there.

May goes. Carly bends down to pick up Liam's shoe.

Carly: I know, darling, they're too tight, eh? That May is driving me mad, by the way.

Liam: Moo.

Carly: Naw – she's not a cow. She means well. It's just she's always telling me what to do...

Carly suddenly spots a tenner under Liam's pushchair.

Carly: No way – I've found a tenner, Liam! I don't believe it!

Liam: Free?

Carly: It's more than three, babe. We've got £14.14. We're minted pal! Let's celebrate!

Carly wanders up the High Street, stopping at shop windows, weighing up her options. The dog is following them again.

Carly: Maybe we should buy ten lottery tickets, eh?

She looks through the window of Kim's Kafé.

Carly: Or we could go in and have a wee cake?

She looks in the window of the charity shop.

Carly: Suppose there's no harm in looking...

. . .

In the charity shop: Carly has an armful of tops and is looking at the little Doc Marten boots.

Carly: It says they've never been worn and they're only £5, Liam, so I could get a top as well...

Carly tries on a top.

Carly: It's nice, eh? Maybe someone will ask me out now?

They stand outside House Heaven. The dog has his paws on the glass.

Liam: Hungry, mama.

Carly: I know I'm just looking. We'll go back for your shoes and a cake at Kim's, okay?

A salesman comes to the door. The dog goes crazy – growling and baring his teeth.

Man: Is that your dug?

Carly: Naw – I don't know whose he is.

Man: He's in here all the time. He's a menace.

Carly: He just follows us around sometimes.

Man: The other day I caught him peeing on a 42-inch plasma... Go on, get tae!

The dog backs off but keeps growling. The man smiles.

Man: I've seen you looking in the window, too. What do you fancy?

Carly: Naw – I'm just looking.

Man: Come and have a wee look inside, then.

Carly: Well, maybe a wee look...

The debt collector watches Carly as she goes in.

Kim's Kafé: There is a big tin sitting on the counter top. It bears a label with the legend, 'Kylie' written on it. The ladies clink cups.

May: Here's to the Kylie!

Angie: The Kylie! Are we really going to put in a fiver a week, but?

Kim: Aye, that's £15 a week between us...

May: £60 a month.

Angie: How much you reckon that tin holds?

May: Hundreds, easy. If we saved for a while...

Dani: And if you shared the kitty, you could buy a second-hand computer.

Angie: What for?

Dani: Kim could get wi-fi and folk could come and surf.

Kim: No danger. You can stick your web up your Apps!

Dani: But you charge folk for using the internet.

Kim: Oh, is that right?

Dani: So if you all invested you could share the profits.

Angie: Hey, where did she get her brains from, May?

May: I don't know – maybe her dad wasn't as thick as he looked.

Kim: Here, that mangy dog is going nuts outside House Heaven.

Dani: I just saw Carly go in there.

May: Aw naw – I hope she doesn't sign anything. I feel sick just thinking about the bills coming in...

Dani: That sofa costs £1371.24 with all the interest.

May: That's a holiday.

Kim: That's a lot of things for her and the boy.

Angie: That's a beautiful leather sofa, if that's what she wants.

May: Aye, if that's what she wants, I suppose.

Inside House Heaven, an emporium of shiny things: Carly stands in awe. The dog goes mental outside.

Man: So, it's the Princess Three-Seater you're after?

Carly: I'm thinking about it.

Man: We need proof of your address and your income, of course.

Carly: See, I'm on benefits...

Man: Not a problem. It's just an extra form to fill in.

Carly: I'm no good at filling in forms...

Man: That's what I'm here for – to help you.

Carly: I don't know. I've other things to pay for too...

What should
Carly do?

Ending One: Carly Decides To...?

Carly's flat: The Princess Three-Seater has pride of place. There is also a new TV and a music centre. Dani sits on the sofa while Carly and Liam dance around, music blaring.

Carly: Doesn't Lady Gaga sound magic on the iPlayer?

Dani: Yeah, your place looks nice, Carly.

Liam: Gaga!

Carly: That's right, baby – Lady Gaga!

Dani: It must have cost you a fortune.

Carly: Naw, it's only a few pounds a week for everything.

Dani: Will you not be paying it off for ages?

Carly: I don't mind. It's worth it.

Liam: Gaga!

Dani: Do you fancy going to see her at the SECC?

Carly: No chance! Have you seen how much the tickets cost?

Dani: We could save up...

Carly: I've got to pay my bills, Dani.

Dani: I'm good with sums. I could look at your bills and see if you can save somewhere?

Carly: It's under control, Dani – and we've got our own club right here, eh Liam?

* * *

Liam watches TV as Carly stands at the door talking to the debt collector again.

Ending Two: Carly Decides To...?

Carly's flat: Everything is falling apart as before but it's tidy and there's a nice throw on the moth-eaten sofa. May and Carly drink coffee and Liam plays on the floor.

May: So are you still getting trouble from those debt collectors?

Carly: No – I've arranged to pay a bit off every month.

May: That's good... This cover on the sofa is lovely.

Carly: I got it from the charity shop. It's not the same as a new sofa.

May: Better off paying off the debts, eh?

Carly: I'm still saving for a sofa, though.

May: We miss seeing you guys out and about, you know...

Carly: We go out. We go to the park. It's free.

May: And Jamie was asking after you...

Carly: I told you, I'm saving up. I'm happy staying in.

May: You still need to have a bit of fun though, eh?

Carly: I want Liam to have a nice home.

May: I bet Liam doesn't care about new sofas, doll.

Carly: Aye, you're probably right...

May: Are you sure you don't fancy a wee coffee at Kim's?

Carly: I don't know... Maybe next week, eh?

* * *

May leaves. Liam watches TV. Carly sits on her sofa, chin in hand and staring into space.

Ending Three: Carly Decides To...?

Kim's Kafé: All the usual suspects are there. Carly is at the counter putting a fiver into the 'Kylie' tin.

Kim: There you go Carly – another fiver in the 'Kylie'.

May: And you'll have that nice sofa in no time too, eh?

Carly: You're kidding? It'll take me a hundred years at the rate I'm going.

Angie: Aye, you'll be needing a Stannah Stair Lift by then!

May: Don't you listen to her, doll. Some things are worth waiting for.

Carly: It's just depressing, though, living in a dump.

May: Well then, you should go out more!

Carly: Can't afford it can I? I'm saving for a sofa...

Kim: Here, there's that boy staring in again.

Angie: Which boy?

Kim: The one that fancies Carly.

Angie: It's Jamie! 'Jamie and Carly up a tree'.

Carly: Shut up! Honestly, why do I come here?

May: Because it beats being home alone... Hey Jamie, come here a minute...

*** ***

Jamie comes in and Carly chats with him over a coffee.

Jamie's Story - The Other Side of the Coin

Monday - £8.23

Jamie comes out the main door of his block of flats. He squints in the daylight, lights a fag, sees the dog and scratches his ears.

Jamie: Awright, dug? I'm going to the buroo, if you fancy a walk?

Jamie continues down the street with the dog. He sees Angie having a fag outside Kim's Kafé.

Jamie: Morning, Angie – how you doing?

Angie: Ocht, not bad, Jamie. How about yourself? Keeping out of trouble?

Jamie: Doing my best, Angie, doing my best.

Angie: Aye, good for you, son. Where are you off to the now?

Jamie: Down the Jobcentre.

Angie: Well good luck with that. It's no easy finding a job these days, eh?

Jamie: No – not with a record, anyway.

Angie: Aye well, keep your nose clean and something will turn up, eh?

Jamie: Maybe, aye.

Angie: Here, is that your dog?

Jamie: Naw – I think he's a stray. Hangs out with me sometimes.

At the Jobcentre: Jamie and Brian wait their turn. May and Carly are chatting near them.

Jamie: There she is, Brian ma man. Girl of my dreams.

Brian: Is she not a bit old for you?

Jamie: Not my auntie May! I mean Carly, ya numpty.

Brian: Pretty girl.

Jamie: She's not pretty, man – she's gorgeous.

Brian: Ask her out then, Jamie.

Jamie: No chance.

Brian: Don't tell me – her boyfriend is six foot four?

Jamie: No, he's out the picture...

Brian: Oh, I get it – scared she'll knock you back!

Jamie: As if, man! Naw, the problem is I've got £8.23 'til my buroo money comes in on Wednesday.

Brian: Ask her out on Thursday, then.

Jamie: Aye, that'll be shining. Are you taking the wife out when your buroo comes in?

Brian: No, I'm paying the electricity bill before they cut me off. Happy days, eh?

Jamie: Aye, it sucks, man.

Brian: It's my kids I feel bad for... Not many treats for them these days.

Jamie: Aye, but they see you more now, man. Now you're not so busy running your 'Empire'.

Brian: 'Empire', eh? I thought it was just a cab company I had...

Brian and Jamie stroll along the High Street, followed by the dog.

Jamie: Maybe your business will pick up again?

Brian: Aye, but I've lost the cabs now. Fancy nicking me one?

Jamie: No danger! I'm not going back to jail, man.

Brian: Sorry, son, I was only joking...

Jamie: I met Carly's ex-boyfriend when I was in there.

Brian: Oh yes? Bit of a bad boy is he?

Jamie: He's a total radge, man. I just robbed cars...

Brian: Someone nicked my car once.

Jamie: Oh aye, what was it?

Brian: 2003 Jaguar, X-type, 2.2 litre.

Jamie: Aye, sounds like something I'd take for a joyride. Sorry, man.

Brian: I probably deserved it. Back then I was what you you would call a 'smug git'.

Jamie: You're awright now, man. Now you're bankrupt.

Brian: And all my cars have been repossessed...

Jamie: See when my lottery numbers come up, I'll buy you a new one.

Brian: After you've taken Carly out?

Jamie: Aye, and after I've bought my BMW. I need a Beamer, man.

Brian and Jamie stop at the newsagent's. As they go in Carly and Liam are coming out.

Jamie: Hiya Liam, my wee pal. How you doing?

Liam: Sweetie?

Carly: How many times, Liam? No! Sorry, Jamie... See you later.

Brian and Jamie enter the shop.

Brian: 'Jamie and Carly up a tree...'

Jamie: Shut up, man – how old are you?

Mushtak: Afternoon, lads.

Jamie: Awright, Mushtak? You going to sell me the winning lottery ticket today?

Mushtak: I'll do my best, pal.

Brian: Waste of bloody money, if you ask me.

Jamie: Aye, you won't be saying that on Wednesday when I win the seven million rollover.

Brian: Do you have any idea how poor those odds are?

Mushtak: It's just a bit of fun, isn't it?

Brian: How's that £8.23, mate? Burning a hole in your pocket?

Jamie: That's £7.23 now, man. I'm investing a pound. Gotta be in it to win it!

The Stag's Head: Brian and Jamie sit at the bar. Pavel is behind it.

Jamie: Two pints please, Pavel and put it on my tab!

Pavel: I'm not running tabs any more, Jamie.

Jamie: Oh right... No bother, I've got cash.

Brian: I'll get these...

Jamie: Naw, man. I want to buy you a pint in return for some advice.

Brian: You want some help with your CV again?

Jamie: Naw – see I did this small business start-up course when I was in the tin pail.

Brian: The what?

Pavel: The jail, mate.

Brian: Oh right... And you want business advice?

Pavel: Here, did you not go bankrupt?

Jamie: It wasn't his fault, was it, Bri?

Brian: Well, I could have just stuck with the six cabs I used to have...

Pavel: But more cabs, more money, eh?

Brian: Yup... I took out loans to buy them and, in the end, the repayments cost more than I was earning.

Pavel: Aye, it's shocking how they kid on those loans are a good deal...

Brian: Anyway, what's your idea, Jamie?

Jamie: I thought maybe a garage. I trained as a mechanic, you know.

Brian: Really?

Jamie: Aye, man - where do you think I learnt to hot-wire a car?

Brian: It's tough starting up on your own, Jamie.

Jamie: Who else is going to give me a job, man?

Brian: I don't know but if you're serious, you need to save some money.

Jamie: Okay, you can buy your own pint, then.

Brian: Fair enough. I better get going, I need to make the kids' tea.

Jamie: You are under the thumb, my friend!

Brian: It's only fair, mate - my wife's the one working. How about a pint tomorrow night?

Jamie: Aren't you forgetting my cash-flow problem?

Brian: It's the wife's book club night. She'll give me a tenner to clear out of the house.

Jamie: That's a sweet deal!

Brian: I'm not complaining. See you tomorrow, then?

Jamie: Aye, maybe...

Brian: We can discuss your business plan. At least I know what not to do, eh?

Brian exits as Tam enters the pub.

Pavel: Here he comes – our very own lottery winner.

Jamie: Who, Tam the Jakey? You're kidding?

Pavel: They say he won £90,000 ten years back.

Jamie: Where's he hiding the cash, then?

Pavel: It's all spent, mate.

Jamie: On what? Not on soap that's for sure.

Pavel: Aye – he could do with a wash, right enough.

Tam: Awright, boys?

Pavel: Alright, Tam, you know I'm no good for credit any more, so don't ask.

Tam: Don't you worry, son – just had a wee bit of luck on the ponies.

Jamie: How much did you win?

Tam: Enough, my friend, enough. Do you like a wee flutter yourself?

Pavel: Here we go...

Tam: Got a magic tip on a long-shot for the 2.30 at Musselburgh tomorrow, if you're interested.

Jamie: Oh aye?

Tam: Aye – 12 to 1 on a wee beauty called 'Bang on the Door'. My pal says she's a dead cert to win.

Jamie: I've got a fiver to my name, Tam.

Income from?

Tam: Well, a fiver will get you £65 at those odds, pal.

Jamie: It's tempting, eh, Pavel?

Pavel: You're better off spending you money on soap, if you ask me.

Jamie: You might be right there, Pav. See you later.

Pavel: Aren't you forgetting something, Jamie?

Jamie: Oh aye – £2.20 isn't it? Daylight robbery!

Jamie pays and leaves, passing the two dogs under the table.

Big Dog: Here, are you about finished?

Wee Dog: Aye – don't know what I ate there but it wasn't a crisp...

Big Dog: Aw mingin! Fancy that walk up the park?

Wee Dog: Aye, why not? Could do with sobering up. Here, is that your shoe there?

Big Dog: Thanks, aye – it belongs to a wee pal of mine.

Wee Dog: Man's best friend, eh?

Big Dog: Aye, wee Liam's always good for a Smartie or his last Rolo...

Wee Dog: What are 'odds', then?

Big Dog: Seriously, do you not know anything? Brain the size of a cat...

The dogs head off.

What are the
odds really?

Jamie is wandering down the street. Davey calls to him from a dark alleyway.

Davey: Jamie... Hey Jamie, man – down here.

Jamie: Who's that...? Oh, it's you Davey.

Davey: Awright, man? I heard you were out.

Jamie: A few months now.

Davey: What you up to?

Jamie: Not much. Signing on, you know.

Davey: Being a good boy, eh?

Jamie: That's the plan, aye.

Davey: You'll be skint, then?

Jamie: I've had better days.

Davey: You know what they say – crime does pay.

Jamie: Davey, man, I'm done with that...

Davey: It's just a wee job. 'Cash in hand'.

Jamie: No thanks, Davey.

Davey: Just a wee delivery tomorrow. Easy money...

Jamie: Aye, but it's not though, is it?

Davey: Fifty quid and only an hour out your life.

Jamie: Fifty?

Davey: Aye – and there'll be more work later on, maybe.

Jamie: I don't know...

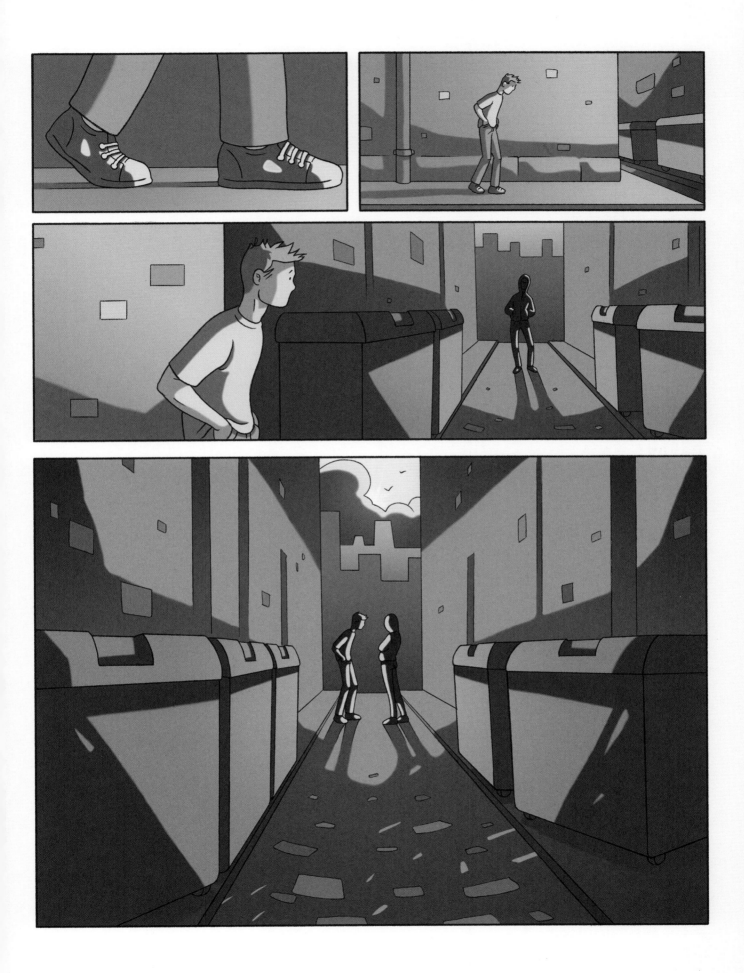

Davey: I'll meet you outside The Stag's Head. Eleven o'clock suit you?

Jamie: Listen, Davey...

Davey: Then I can take you down to meet the boys.

Jamie: I'll think about it.

The scruffy dog suddenly appears, going mental at Davey.

Davey: Hey, get off me, ya wee...

Jamie: Here dug! Come on, come here!

Davey: Is this your mangy mutt?

Jamie: Naw – he just hangs about with me sometimes.

Davey: Aye, you're a lucky dog... Jamie's just saved you from a kickin. See you tomorrow, pal...

Jamie: I'll have to see, Davey.

Davey: Aye right! See you tomorrow.

Davey leaves. The dog looks at Jamie.

Jamie: I know what you're thinking, dug, but I'm skint, pal.

The dog drops Liam's shoe at Jamie's feet.

What's this you're giving me, a shoe...? Hey doesn't that belong to Carly's wee boy...?

The park, as before: Damien and Dani are hanging out by the swings. Carly sits on a bench with Liam. The dog is eating Liam's sandwich. Jamie appears with Liam's shoe.

Jamie: Hey, Carly, are you looking for this?

Carly: Aye, where did you find it?

Jamie: The dog had it. It's a bit manky, like.

Carly: Great. Now I'm covered in dog slaver... I'm going home.

Jamie: I was going for a poke of chips, if you fancy...?

Carly: Thanks, but I'm not in the mood for chips.

Jamie is left alone with the dog. He sits on the bench. The dog offers Jamie a comforting paw...

Jamie: Smooth, eh dug? Really smooth.

Dani and Damien stroll past Jamie on the bench.

Damien: Crashed and burned, eh mate?

Jamie: What are you talking about?

Damien: I'm talking about you having nae luck with the lovely Carly.

Dani: She's really nice, eh?

Jamie: She's awright.

Dani: You should ask her out properly, like...

Damien: Aye, somewhere fancy – girls like that.

Dani: It doesn't have to be fancy!

Damien: Yeah it does, or you have no chance...

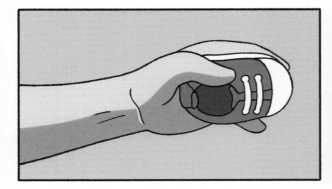

Jamie: Shut up, you pair, eh? Come on dug, if you're coming.

Jamie slopes off with dog and a cloud over his head.

Damien: See, that's the trouble with women – they cost money.

Dani: No they don't!

Damien: Aye they do – they always want you to pay.

Dani: What century are you from? Girls pay...

Damien: Aye right.

Dani: Come on then, I'll take you to the pictures. I can use my card.

Damien: You got a credit card?

Dani: No, my Young Scot card. I've got a money off voucher for the cinema.

Damien: Last of the big spenders, eh?

Dani: At least my mum doesn't buy my shoes!

Damien: Naw - she gets you old shite from the charity shop!

Dani: So? I get stuff there too and I bet I save up for a deposit for a flat before you do.

Damien: Aye? Well you'll be living alone with your mingin old clothes.

Dani: Oh shut up, you muppet...! Are you coming or what?

Damien: Told you, you like me really.

Dani: Really, Damien, I don't.

What's in a wallet?

Tuesday - £5.03

Jamie stands outside the main door of his flat. He can see Carly, Liam and the dog outside House Heaven. The dog is going mental at the salesman. Jamie looks at the £5.03 in his hand and takes out his fag packet. It's empty. He crumples it up.

Jamie: Great - out of fags. Looks like another crap day in the life of Jamie Mack...

* * *

Mushtak is sorting out his veg display. He spots Jamie.

Mushtak: Morning Jamie!

Jamie: Awright Mush?

Mushtak: The usual for you, this morning?

Jamie: No thanks, mate.

Mushtak: No fags, eh?

Jamie: I've got a fiver to my name... Probably a good day to give them up.

Mushtak: Until you get your Giro, eh? Aw no - here's that dog again!

Jamie: He's awright. He's my wee pal.

Mushtak: Aye? Well your 'wee pal' nicked a packet of sausages off me yesterday.

Jamie: Hiya Dug - did Carly tell you to get lost, then? I know the feeling...

Jamie and the dog peer in the window of Kim's Kafé. The women are starting their menodge.

Jamie: I know, dug, I'm starving... But also totally skint.

Jamie and the dog reach the bookies. Tam is outside having a fag, clearly the worse for wear.

Tam: Aye-aye, Jamie lad – here to put a fiver on the 2.30? 'Bang on the Door' – that's the girl!

Jamie: I don't know. I don't fancy the name.

Tam: How no...? Aw, does it remind you of the polis coming round to your house?

Jamie: Naw, it reminds me of those women my Auntie May didnae like.

Tam: What women?

Jamie: The ones who used to come round to your house offering to lend you money.

Tam: Oh, did May get in a spot of bother with them?

Jamie: Aye, we used to have to hide every time there was a knock on the door.

Tam: Let's play, 'we're no home', eh?

Jamie: May says once you're with them, they never leave you alone.

Tam: Women never off your doorstep? Sounds magic!

Jamie: Not if you owe them money, pal.

Tam: Well, I'm on a winning streak. Four in a row! You'll be laughing lad, I'm telling you...

Jamie stops outside The Stag's Head. He looks round nervously. May appears out of nowhere.

May: Morning, Jamie!

Jamie: Auntie May, you nearly gave me a heart attack!

May: Sorry, son. I saw you looking through the café window. You looked hungry.

Jamie: I'm fine, thanks.

May: Do you not fancy breakfast – my treat?

Jamie: I can't, Auntie May. I'm busy.

May: Is it not a bit early for a drink?

Jamie: I'm not going in. I'm waiting for someone.

May: Oh aye? Who you waiting for?

Jamie: Just someone.

May: Who?

Jamie: A guy I know, okay?

May: A friend, is it?

Jamie: Just a guy.

May: Here, are you in trouble again, Jamie?

Jamie: No! Honestly Auntie May... It's about a job, okay?

Pavel arrives to open up the pub.

Pavel: Jamie - just the lad I wanted to see! Bit early for you, is it not, May?

May: I'm not stopping. I'll see you later...

Pavel: Are you and the girls coming to the quiz tonight?

May: Aye definitely! See you then.

Pavel: Nice lady, your auntie.

Jamie: Aye, always manages to stick her nose into my business, but.

Pavel: Now that's what I wanted to talk to you about. Come on in.

Jamie: Business?

Pavel: Aye. The quiz is always busy and I could use an extra pair of hands.

Jamie: I don't know...

Pavel: Just five hours and I'll pay you £6 an hour.

Jamie: I can't, Pav. The folk from the buroo drink in here sometimes. I'll get in trouble.

Pavel: You can declare it as a one-off job. I'll pay cash in hand...

Jamie: They'll take it off my money, and I'll end up more skint next week.

Pavel: I just wanted to give you a go, eh?

Jamie: A go?

Pavel: Aye - did I not hear your pal Brian say you needed a job?

90

Jamie: Yeah, but I need something full-time. I need to
pay the rent and put some by...

Pavel: Well, you could try it tonight and if it works
out, I'll give you more hours.

Jamie: Aye?

Pavel: I could put you through the books. You'd be legit.
National Insurance, tax – the lot.

Jamie: That'd be a first...

Pavel: I pay just over the minimum wage, but it's still
more than you get from the buroo, eh?

Tam comes in.

Tam: I just canny lose today! Have you put your bet on
yet, Jamie-boy?

Davey comes in.

Pavel: Hey, Davey, you're barred! Go on, out!

Davey: I'm just here to pick up my pal Jamie. Are you
ready, Jamie?

Jamie: I need to think a minute, Davey...

Davey: What's to think about? I just saw that Carly, by
the way. She's nice, eh?

**What should
Jamie do?**

Ending One – Jamie Decides To...?

Jamie is talking to a shadowy figure in a dark back room.

Boss: Well, Jamie – Davey says you're doing a grand job.

Jamie: I'm doing my best...

Boss: Nice to have a bit of cash in your pocket, eh?

Jamie: Aye.

Boss: Davey tells me you've got a bird on the go?

Jamie: Aye.

Boss: He says she's a looker. I bet she likes the finer things in life.

Jamie: Carly's not like that.

Boss: They're all like that, pal, trust me. Davey says you know your way around a motor?

Jamie: I'm a mechanic, aye.

Boss: I've a car that needs a clean-up and a re-spray, if you get my meaning?

Jamie: I'm happy with what I'm doing, thanks, boss.

Boss: There's more money in this work, of course...

Jamie: Right.

Boss: Don't worry – it's perfectly legal...

* * *

Outside Jamie's tenement. Police lights are flashing and a policeman is talking to Jamie. May and Angie look on and Carly is standing nearby, holding on to Liam.

Ending Two – Jamie Decides To...?

Jamie and Tam are outside the bookies.

Jamie: Yeeeeeeehah! £65! Tam, my man – you are a legend!

Tam: I told you son, I'm on a winning streak and I've a tip on another long-shot...

Jamie: I don't know, maybe I should quit while I'm ahead?

Tam: Good odds – 10 to 1. Put your winnings on and your looking at over £600.

Jamie: Unless we lose, of course.

Brian arrives.

Brian: Morning, lads – you look happy.

Jamie: Brian, man, I've just won £60! Not bad, eh?

Brian: I'll expect a pint tonight, then. Unless you're taking Carly out instead?

Jamie: I don't know. Maybe if I win another race...

Tam: We'd better get in there, if you're coming, James?

Jamie: Okay. I'll see you later, Brian... And I'll get you a pint, don't worry!

Brian: I won't bet on it...

* * *

Some time later: Tam is leaning against a wall, looking the worse for wear again. Jamie is kicking the wall in fury and frustration.

Ending Three – Jamie Decides To...?

The Stag's Head: Pavel and Jamie are behind the bar. Brian sits on a barstool. May, Kim and Angie are at a table doing a quiz.

Brian: Pavel says you're doing a grand job.

Jamie: I'm doing my best...

Brian: Nice to have a bit of money in your pocket, eh?

Jamie: Aye, it doesn't go very far, though.

Pavel: Hey, I told you – you'll get a pay rise when you've done a full month!

Jamie: Brilliant – me and Carly will celebrate with a whole tin of baked beans.

Brian: How's it going with the lovely Carly?

Jamie: It's going great but wee Liam costs money, eh?

Brian: I know.

Jamie: I'm not saving much for our small-business fund.

Brian: We'll get there in the end, eh?

Jamie: Aye – in fifty years. How many 75-year-old mechanics do you know?

Brian: Could be worse. I heard your pal Davey is back in the tin pail.

* * *

Jamie and Carly sit on a park bench with Liam. The scruffy dog sleeps at their feet. Jamie talks about his dream of a garage.

Glossary

A -   **aye** – (Scots) yes

      awright – (Scots) all right, alright

B -   **barred** – banned from entering somewhere

      bird – (slang) girl or woman

      bookies – bookmakers, betting shop

      bling – (slang) flashy and showy accessories

      buroo – (Scots slang) - The Jobcentre or Employment Office. Unemployment or Social Security benefit

C -   **canny** – (Scots) can not

D -   **doofus** – (slang) someone who hasn't a clue

      DMs – Doc Martens shoes or boots made by 'Dr Marten'

      dug – (Scots) dog

E -   **Eighty Shilling** – a kind of beer

F -   **fag** – (slang) cigarette

      flutter – a small bet or wager

      funpire –(slang) a play on the word 'vampire'- someone who sucks all the fun out of life!

G -   **git** – (slang) annoying or dislikeable person

      get tae – (Scots) go away!

K -   **kitty** – a shared fund of money

M - **manky** – dirty, filthy

menodge – (Scots from the French 'ménage') also monoge or minoge. A kind of savings club

mingin – (Scots) revolting, horrible or unpleasant

minted – (slang) rich, well-off

N - **nae** – (Scots) not any

naw – (Scots) no

natter – to talk, to chatter

numpty – (slang) stupid person

O - **ocht** – (Scots) oh

R - **radge** – (Scots) crazy or angry. A mad or violent person

S - **SECC** – The Scottish Exhibition and Conference Centre

skint – short of money

slaver – (Scots) saliva

smartarse – someone who thinks they're clever

spewin – (Scots) vomiting, being sick

T - **ta** – thanks, thank you

tin pail – (rhyming slang) jail

'That'll be shining' (rhyming slang) – That'll be shining bright – right.

W - **WAG** – the wife or girlfriend of a footballer

wee – (Scots) little

Financial Terms and Definitions

Annual Percentage Rate (APR) - The overall cost of borrowing if you owe money on your credit card, loan or overdraft. The higher the APR the more interest you will pay.

Bankrupt - Bankruptcy is a legal status that usually lasts for a year and is a way of clearing debts you can't pay. Sequestration is the Scottish legal term for bankruptcy. Bankruptcy has a number of consequences. One of these is that the person who has been declared bankrupt hands over the things they own and their financial assets to an appointed trustee, who then sells off whatever is not exempt to pay off the debts.

Benefits - You may be eligible to receive financial and other support from the State if you are on a low income or have certain costs to meet because of your personal situation.

'Cash in hand' - This is a method of payment usually for goods or services. By not declaring this income, people avoid paying tax, National Insurance or VAT. This is deemed as fraud (see 'through the books').

Charity - This refers to 'a good cause' usually funded by contributions from individuals or groups of people.

Cash flow - Cash flow is a business term that refers to the movement of money in and out of an organisation. However a number of lenders use this as a basis for renewing or rolling over loans. The APR charged on these types of loan is usually very high.

Credit - Buying on credit is a form of borrowing. It includes paying by credit card or store card, hire purchase, and other credit agreements including interest-free credit where you 'buy now, pay later'.

Credit card - A plastic card used instead of cash as a method of payment for goods and services. You buy, and then pay later when you receive a statement from the credit card provider showing what you owe. Any balance that is owed at the end of the month will have interest added. This can be a very expensive way to borrow money.

Co-op stamps - This was the way that dividends were paid through being a member of a not-for-profit organisation. These were seen as a loyalty payment, an idea picked up and developed by organisations such as Green Shield Stamps (withdrawn in 1991) and Tesco Clubcard and Boots Advantage Card.

Council Tax - Council Tax helps pay for local services like policing and rubbish collection. It applies to all domestic properties, whether they are owned or rented.

Credit union - This is a financial organisation that lets you save and borrow money. They are owned and run by their members, for their members. Membership depends on people having a common bond based on a geographical area or a place of work.

Debt - This is usually seen as owing money to an individual or company through purchasing goods or services through a credit agreement. There are many reasons for debt and due to the interest normally charged on debt it is essential to manage it effectively or it could grow rapidly causing additional financial problems (see repossessions).

Earnings - These are normally seen as payments for work and are usually taxable. However there is also 'unearned income' from investments and property which are also taxable.

Interest - Interest refers to both the charge made by lenders on money you borrow from them and the amount earned by your savings. Interest can be variable (goes up or down) or it can be fixed.

Invest - The act of putting money aside, which will hopefully grow in value, to provide a long term benefit (see savings).

'Kitty' - This could be seen as the total sum contributed by the members of the 'menodge'. It is distributed to individuals according to the original agreement drawn up.

Lottery - A lottery is a form of gambling which involves the drawing of lots for a prize. In the UK there is a national lottery for a cash prize, it now has the 'lotto' branding. The term lottery can be used to suggest someone is taking a chance/running a risk on something.

Loans - A bank loan is a set amount of money which the bank has agreed to lend you for a set period of time. Payments and interest rates are agreed at the time of the loan. Loans can be secured or unsecured. If a secured loan is not paid then properties can be repossessed.

Minimum wage - The UK has a national minimum wage which legally sets the minimum amount an individual can be paid for an hour's work, this varies according to the worker's age.

Money lenders - These can be legal or illegal. They are perceived to charge very high rates of interest. Often they link the loans and repayments to the individual's 'cash flow'.

'Menodge' - This is a type of savings club where each member contributes a fixed sum for a stated period (other spellings include ménage, monoge and minodge).

National Insurance contributions (NICs) - You pay NICs from your earnings to qualify for certain social security benefits including the State Pension.

Odds - This is the term used to express the chances of winning a bet or staking a play on the lottery.

Rebate (income tax or council tax) - This is a refund due to an individual having paid too much tax. The reason for this is usually changing financial circumstances or an administrative error.

Repossessed - If you buy your home with the help of a secured loan then the lender will usually protect their interest by registering a 'legal charge' against your house. This means that when the house is sold you will first have to repay the lender any money you have outstanding. If you do not keep up the repayments on the loan the lender can repossess your property. This means they can take over the property and sell it in order to pay back the loan.

Repayments - The amount you have to pay back to the lender (usually monthly) when you borrow money.

Rollover - Takes place when the 'jackpot' is not won on the national lottery. A number of money lenders also 'roll over' small loans which are linked to an individual's or household's cash flow.

Savings - There are two ways to save – short term and long term. Savings accounts are for times when you may need to get at your money quickly. They're different from investments, which are really for the longer term.

Share profits - In the story this refers to sharing the 'kitty' from the 'menodge'. However some young people may be aware of different profit sharing procedures in businesses such as partnerships, limited companies (Ltd)and public limited companies (Plc).

Student Loans - This is a financial service offered by the Student Loans Company (SLC) to over one million students annually, in colleges and universities across the four education systems of England, Northern Ireland, Scotland and Wales. Student loans are available to higher education students to help meet their living costs. There is interest charged on the amount you borrow but it is less than a bank or building society would charge you. You don't have to repay your loan until your income reaches a certain level, but beware interest keeps being added until you pay it all back.

Tax - A charge you pay to the government – there are different types of tax but income and inheritance tax are the ones most people are aware of. The other main tax people will be aware of is VAT (Value Added Tax) which is collected by various organisations and businesses and then paid to government.

'Through the books' - this is a term used for 'legitimate' payments for goods and services that will be eligible for income tax, National Insurance or VAT. (see 'cash in hand')

Young Scot Card - The Young Scot National Entitlement Card enables young people, aged 11-26, to access over 1,400 discounts and special offers in Scotland alone and many more in forty-two European countries. In addition, the Card offers cheaper public transport for young people aged sixteen, seventeen and eighteen. The PASS 'proof of age' hologram enables young people to use their card as valid proof of age across the UK.

Author and Illustrators' Biographies

Gowan Calder

Gowan is an actress and playwright. She has acted in theatre,
TV, radio and film and performed in Europe, Asia and America.
Her plays have been produced in theatres throughout Britain and
also broadcast on BBC Radio. Gowan grew up in Edinburgh and
West Lothian and now lives by the sea. She has often been 'skint'.

metaphrog

metaphrog are Sandra Marrs and John Chalmers.
Together, they have been creating comics, graphic novels and
illustrations since 1996, gradually building a loyal following and
receiving critical acclaim worldwide.
John is from Scotland and studied science, gaining several degrees,
including a PhD from Strathclyde University's Electronic and
Electrical Engineering Department in a branch of Opto-Electronics
involving micro-machining.
Sandra is from France and has a degree in Arts and Letters. In 1994,
she moved to Scotland. That same year, John returned from working in
The Netherlands.
Their meeting was a catalyst, and within a few months, they created
metaphrog.
Their 'Louis' series has received several prestigious award
nominations, including three Eisner Award nominations: Best Graphic
Album New, Best Title for a Younger Audience, and Best Colouring, an
Ignatz Award nomination for Best New Talent, and also a YALSA Great
Graphic Novels for Teens 2011 nomination.

Acknowledgements - Trial Groups

Tutor/ Group Leader	Trial Group
Joan Elliott Youth Literacy Tutor Brian Borland Youth Worker South Ayrshire Council	South Ayrshire Youth Forum, Ayr: Andrew Pollock, Carlie McDowall, Carly Wilson, Janet Davidge, Maria McGough and Stephanie Woodcock
Sharon Graham Money Management - Woman's Peer Education Group Tutor	Money Management - Woman's Peer Education Group, Financial Inclusion Team, GEMAP, Easterhouse: Alexis Simpson, Irene Graham, Jean Logan and Rosemarie Lindsay
Ann Swinney Literacies Worker (Young People) Perth and Kinross Council	Learning Curve - A K Bell Library, York Place, Perth: Dawid Modrezjewski, John McIntosh, Jonathan Lindsay, Lea Ali, Oliver Hill, Richard Whalley, Robert Grant, Sarah Bruce and Stephen Walker
Hazel Stevenson Support for Learning Tutor Reid Kerr College	Support for Learning Department, Reid Kerr College, Renfrew Road, Paisley Renfrewshire - Step Students

Acknowledgements - Trial Groups (Continued)

Tutor/ Group Leader	Trial Group
Danielle Ward North Edinburgh Young People's Forum	North Edinburgh Young People's Forum, Edinburgh: Caryn Lumsden, Charmaine Borland, Kayleigh Shaw, Lindsay and Stephaine Lynch
Kenny Harrow and Steve Kay Families Learning (Literacy) and Community Learning and Development	Families Life Long Learning Community Learning and Development, Ardrossan, Ayrshire: Darrel Thomson, Lisa Heenan, Robert Anderson and Vicky Powell
Joe Moran Army Basic Skills Development Manager (Literacy and Numeracy) - Scotland and Northern England	Army Education and Skills Development Unit, Redford Barracks, Colinton, Edinburgh: CPL Thomas Winters, GNR Newman, Pamela Jane Sime, RFN Wildman, RFN Preston and RFN Reay
Angela Fulton and Lucy Sewell AddzUp Representatives from Gemap - Credit Union Ltd and finances support group, 95 Morrison Street, Glasgow	Six pupils from S5 (16-17-year-olds) Lochend High school, Easterhouse, Glasgow
Lorna Callery Reader-in-Residence	Education Support Department Polmont Prison, Falkirk

Acknowledgements - Steering Group Members

Koren Calder Young Adult Project
Coordinator
Philippa Cochrane Learning Team
Manager
Colm Linnane Learning Manager
(Secondment)

Scottish Book Trust
Sandeman House,
Trunk's Close,
55 High Street,
Edinburgh EH1 1SR

Dorothy Ogle
Financial Inclusion Team

Scottish Government Employability
and Tackling Poverty Division
2-E South Victoria Quay,
Edinburgh EH6 6QQ

Daniel Sellers Adult Literacy
Development Officer
Sheila Doogan
Development Officer for
the Young People, Children
and Families team

The Communities Team of Learning
and Teaching Scotland
The Optima Building,
58 Robertson Street,
Glasgow G2 8DU

Jim Lally Director of Scottish
Centre of Financial Education
Kenny Ferguson Development
Officer

Scottish Centre for Financial
Education
Learning and Teaching Scotland
Level 9, City House,
Overgate, Dundee DD1 1UH

Allison Barnes Financial
Capability Manager for Scotland

The Money Advice Service
25 The North Colonnade,
Canary Wharf, London E14 5HS

Alasdair Watt
Financial Awareness Strategy
Officer

Financial Inclusion Team at
Glasgow City Council Development &
Regeneration Services
Glasgow City Council
229 George Street,
Glasgow G1 1QU

Danielle Logan Information
Services Officer

Young Scot
Rosebery House,
9 Haymarket Terrace,
Edinburgh EH12 5EZ

Rona Doig
Tina Livingston
Corporate Responsibility

Standard Life
Standard Life House,
30 Lothian Road,
Edinburgh EH1 2DH

Contacts - Supporting Websites

- BBC Learning - www.bbc.co.uk/learning

- BBC Skillswise - www.bbc.co.uk/skillswise

- Citizens Advice Scotland (CAS) - www.cas.org.uk

- Communities of Practice in Adult Literacies(CoPAL)- www.aloscotland.com

- Family Learning - www.familylearning.org.uk

- Financial Learning Online - www.floscotland.org.uk

- Financial Literacy - Make Money Make Sense - www.moneymakesense.co.uk

- Greater Easterhouse Money Advice Project (GEMAP) - www.ebilitytechnologies.co.uk/jobs/gemap

- Learning and Teaching Scotland - www.ltscotland.org.uk

- The Money Advice Service - www.moneyadviceservice.org.uk

- Money for Life - www.moneyforlifeprogramme.org.uk

- National Youth Information Portal for young people in school - www.youngscot.org

- Scottish Book Trust - www.scottishbooktrust.com/skint

- Scottish Government - www.scotland.gov.uk

- The Financial Literacy Resource Centre - www.financiallit.org

- Workers Educational Association - www.weascotland.org.uk

- Young Scot Extra -information for young people making the transition into independent living - www.youngscotextra.org